Pirate Pete

loses his hat

Written by Susan Akass

Illustrated by Ben Cort

Heinemann

Pete was a pirate.
He had a parrot called Beaky.
Pete had a big pirate hat.

One day the wind blew and blew.
It blew the ship up and down.

'I don't like this wind,' said Pete.
'I don't like this wind,' said Beaky.

The wind blew and blew and blew.
It blew the big hat into the sea.

'Help, help!' said Pete.
'I want my hat.'

Pete got a telescope.

'I can't see my hat,' he said.

'What can you see?' said Beaky.
'I can see a whale,' said Pete.

'What can you see now?' said Beaky.

'I can see a dolphin,' said Pete.

Beaky got the telescope.
'I can see the hat,'
said Beaky.
'Can you?' said Pete.

'Yes,' said Beaky.

'I can see a hat.

And I can see a big shark!'

'Thundering Cannonballs!'
said Pete.